The

M000073523

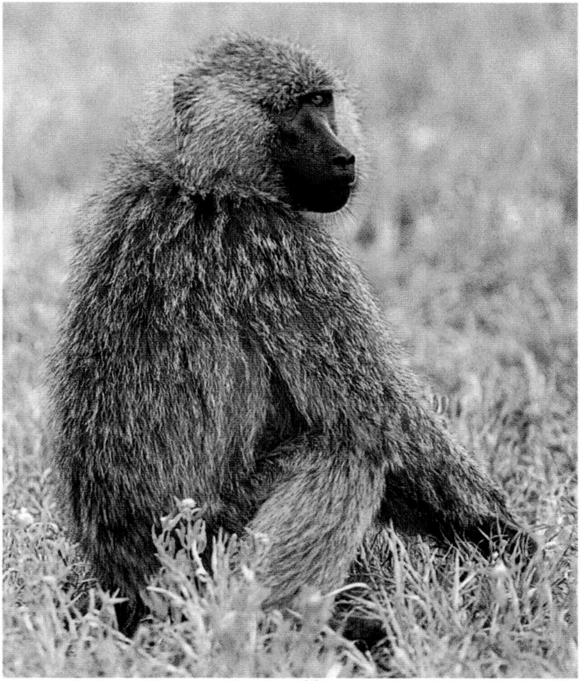

Karen Ortega

Rigby

Look at the monkey.

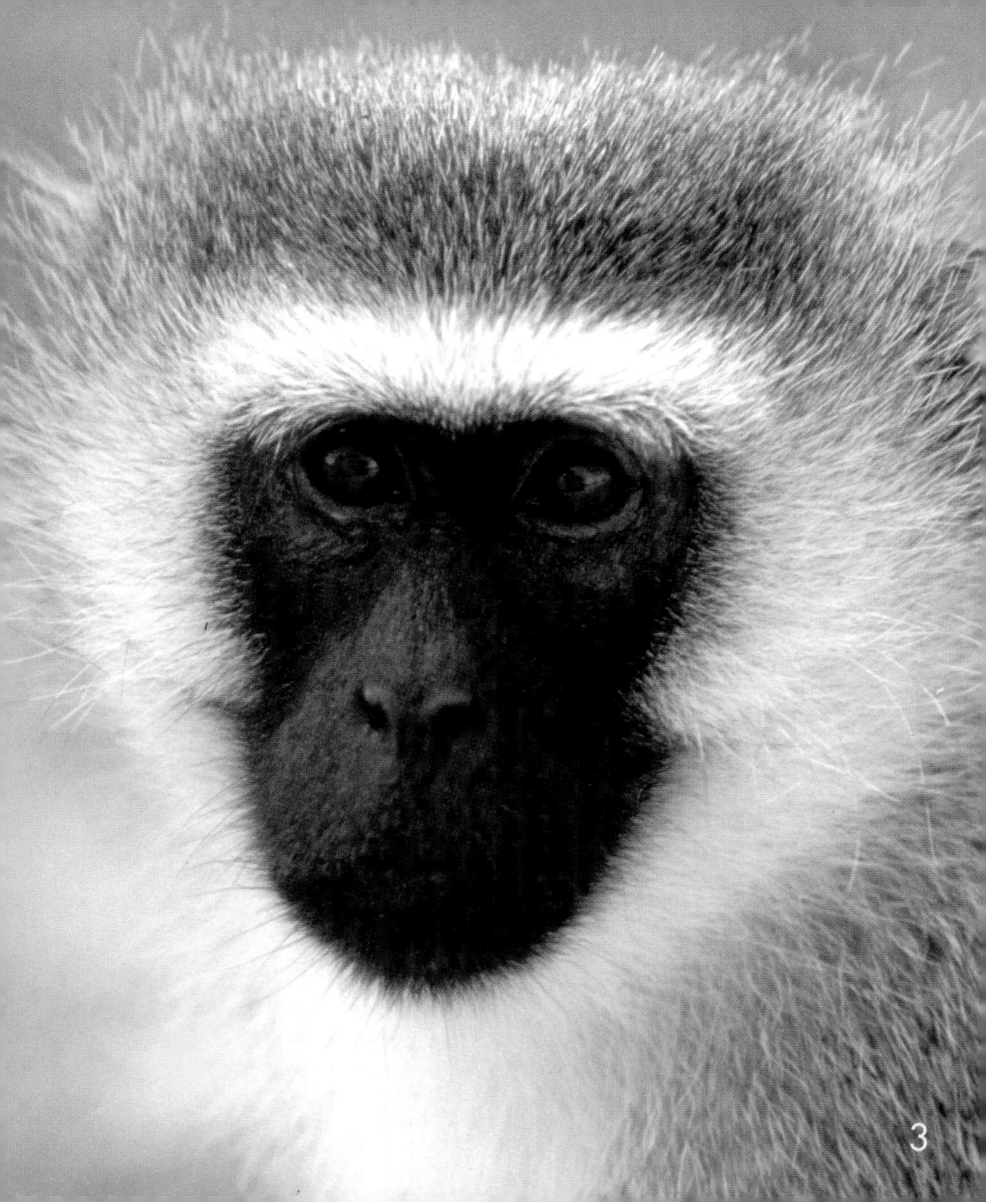

Look at the eyes.

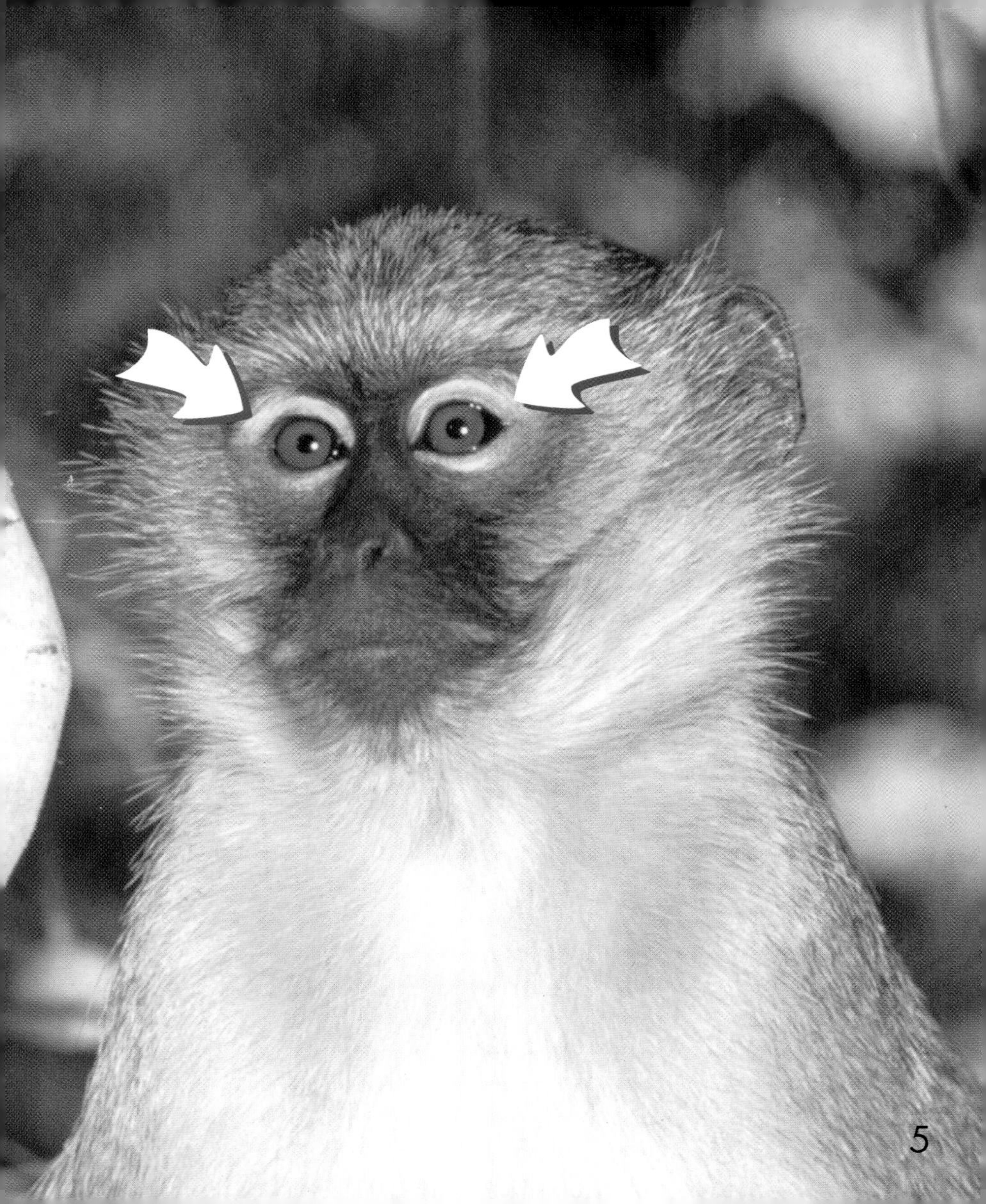

Look at the nose.

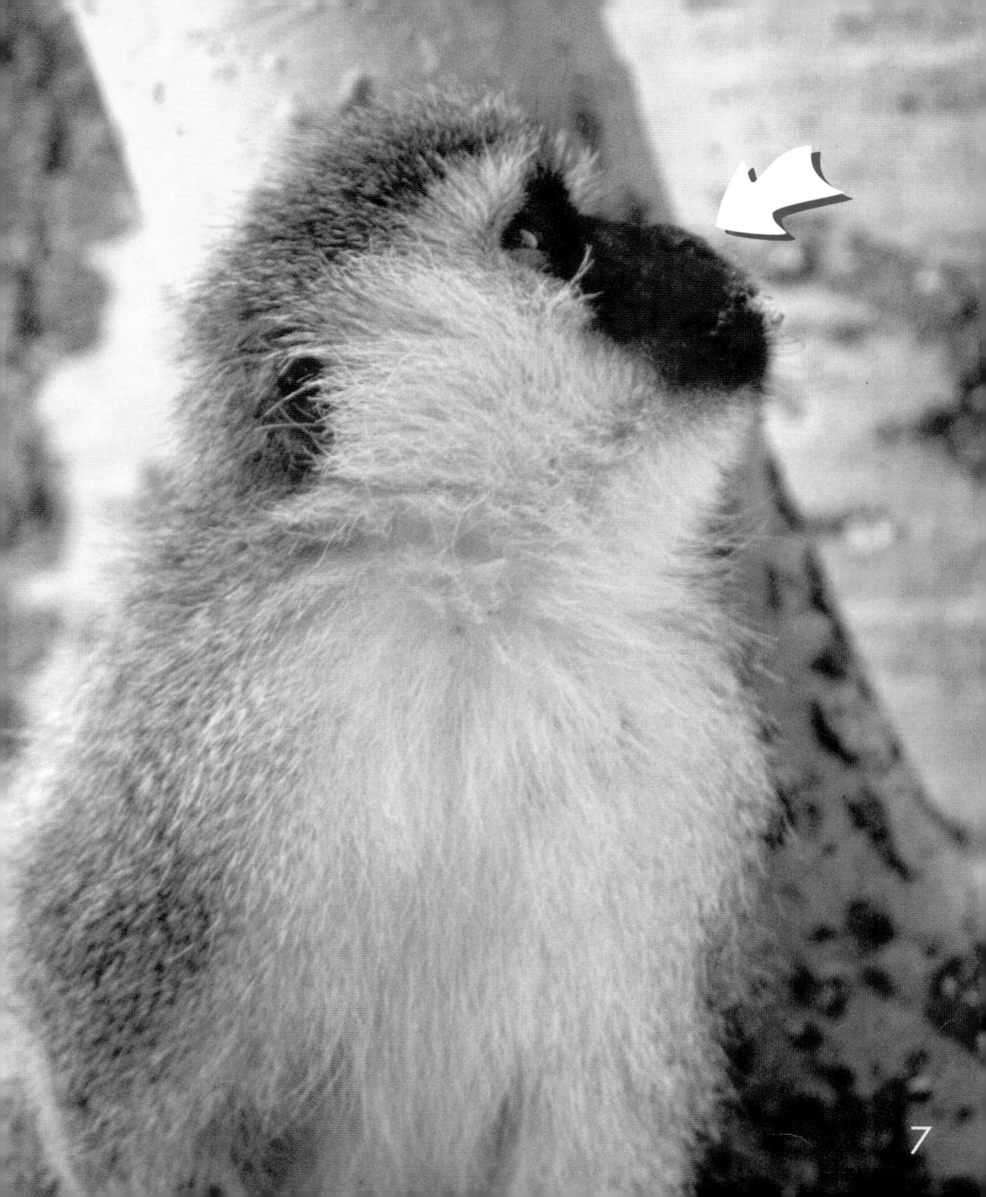

Look at the ears.

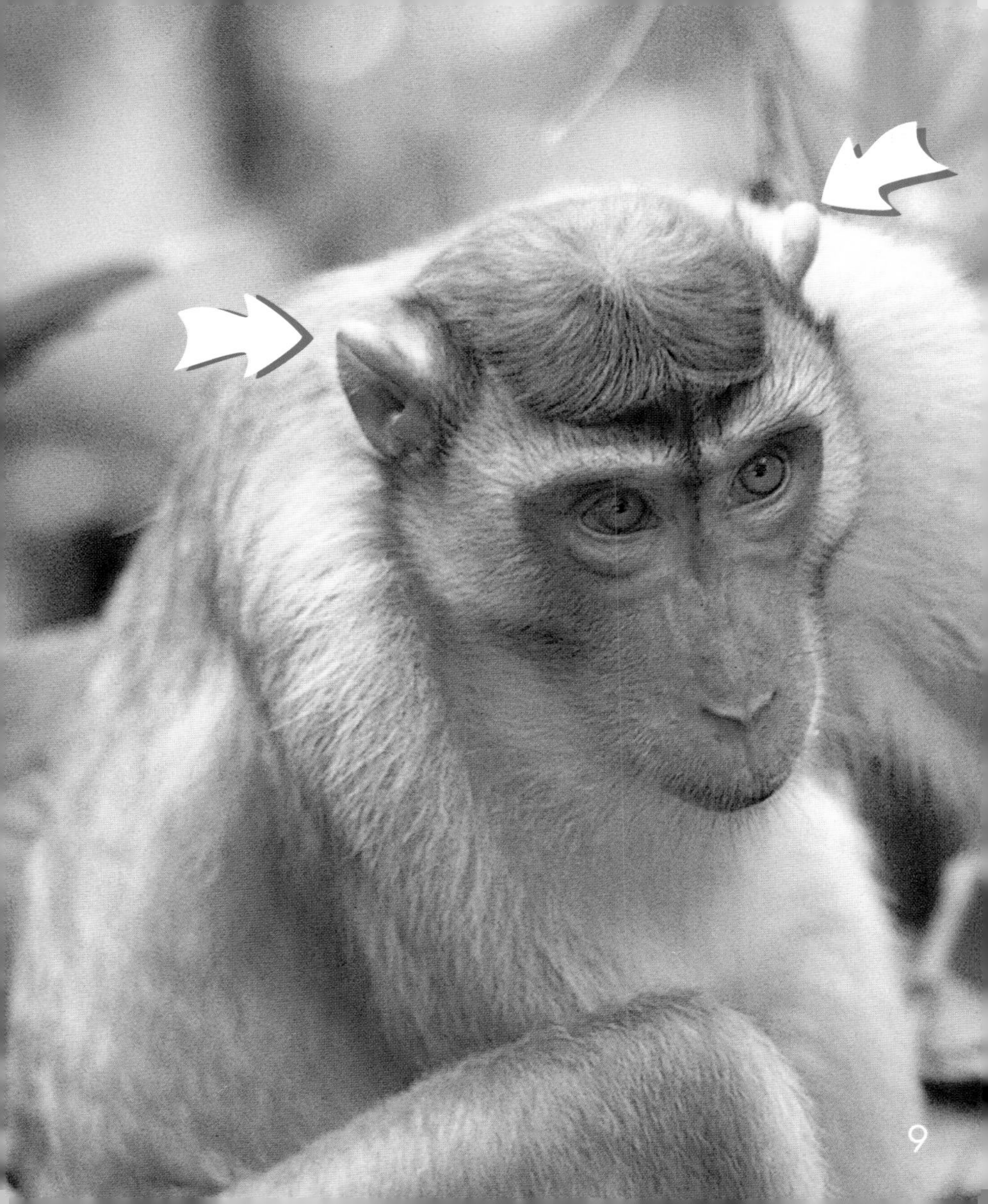

Look at the mouth.

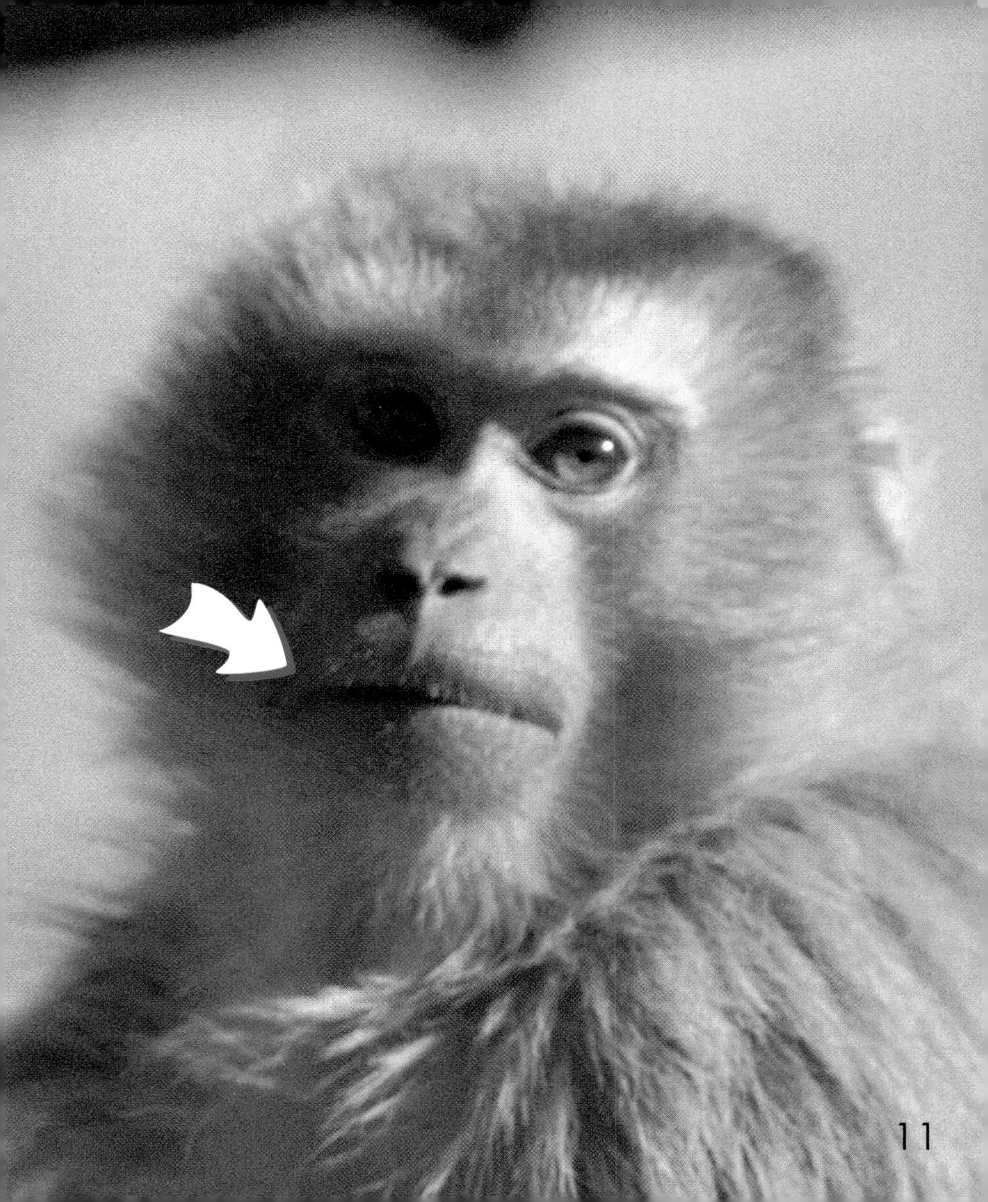

Look at the hands.

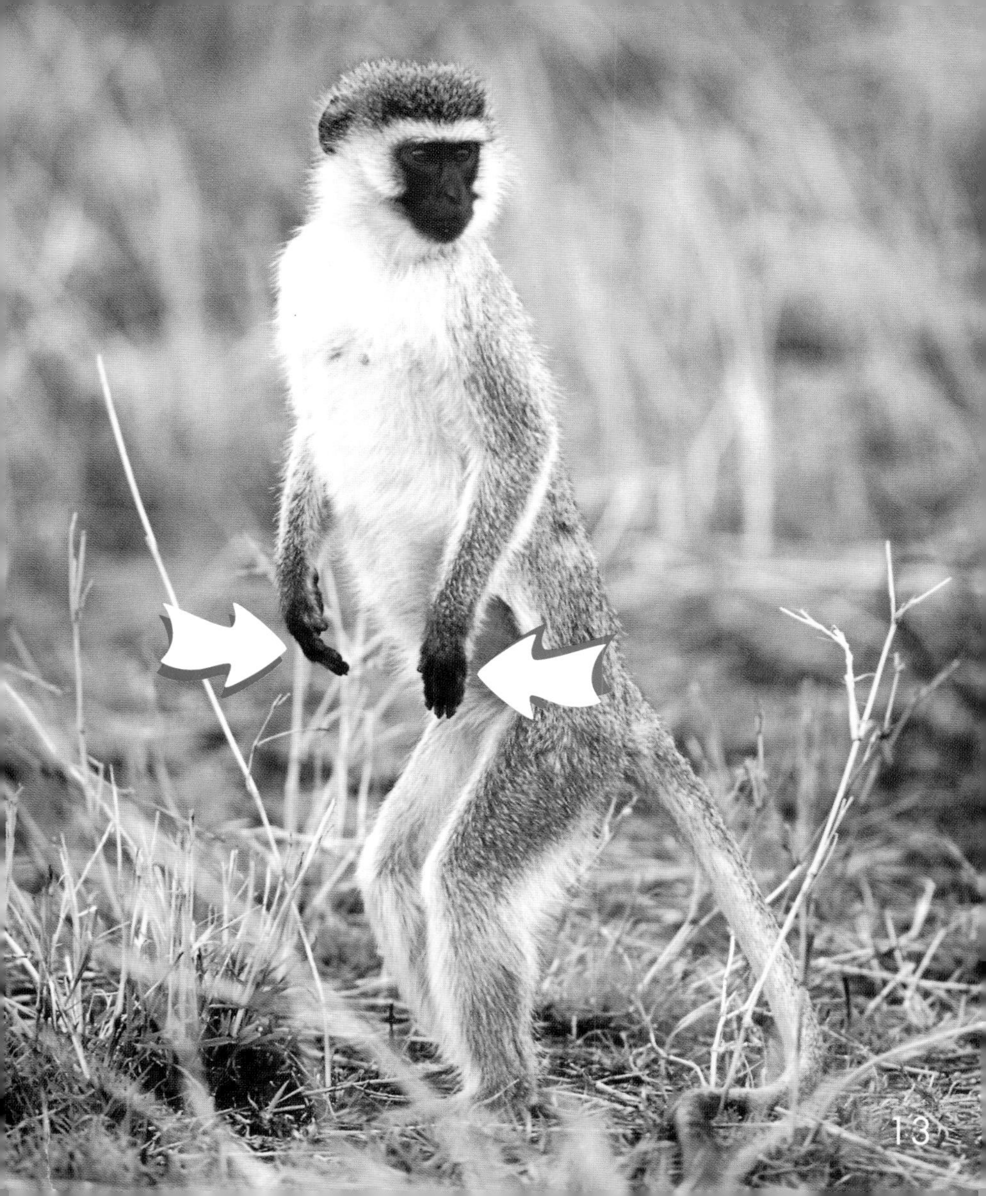

Look at the feet.

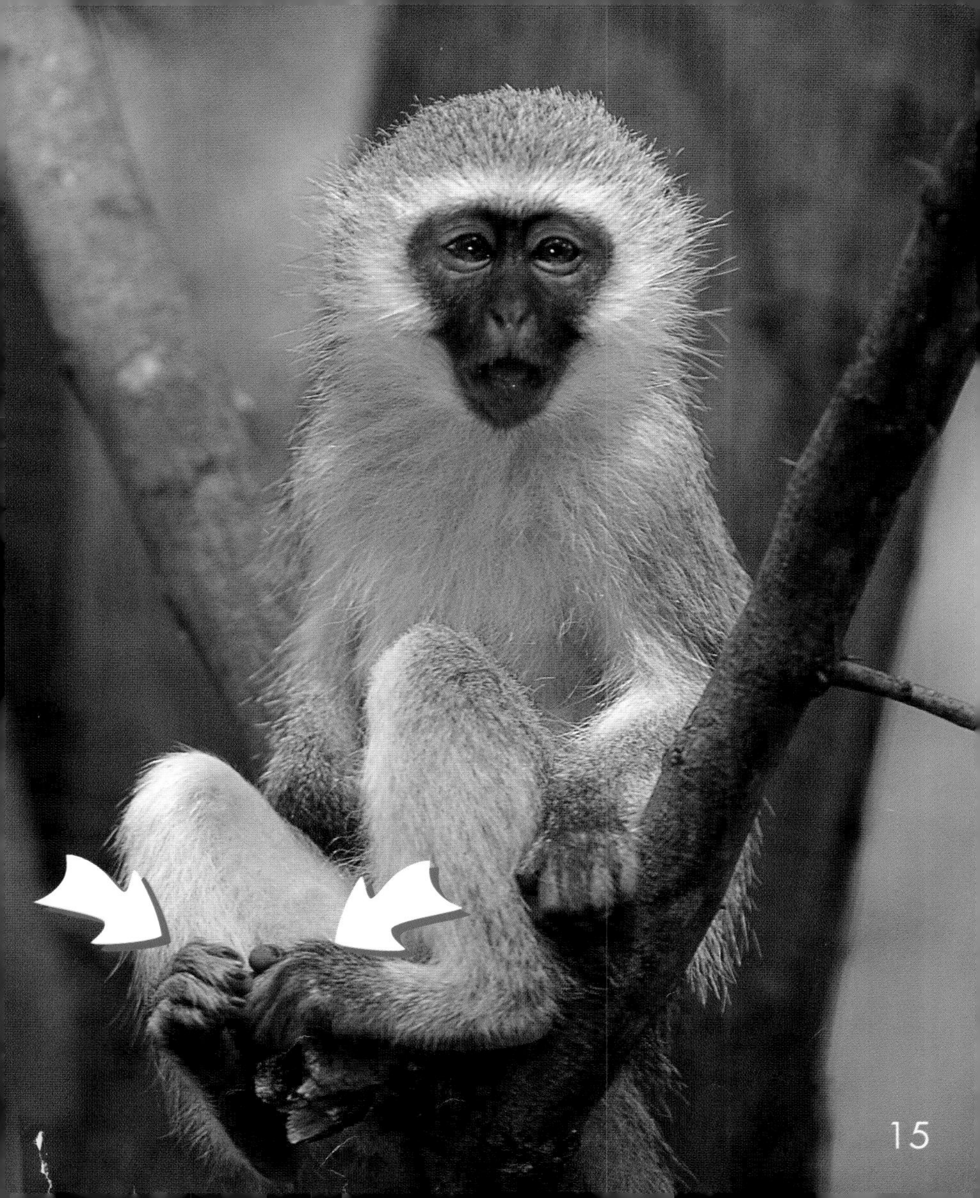

Look at the monkey!

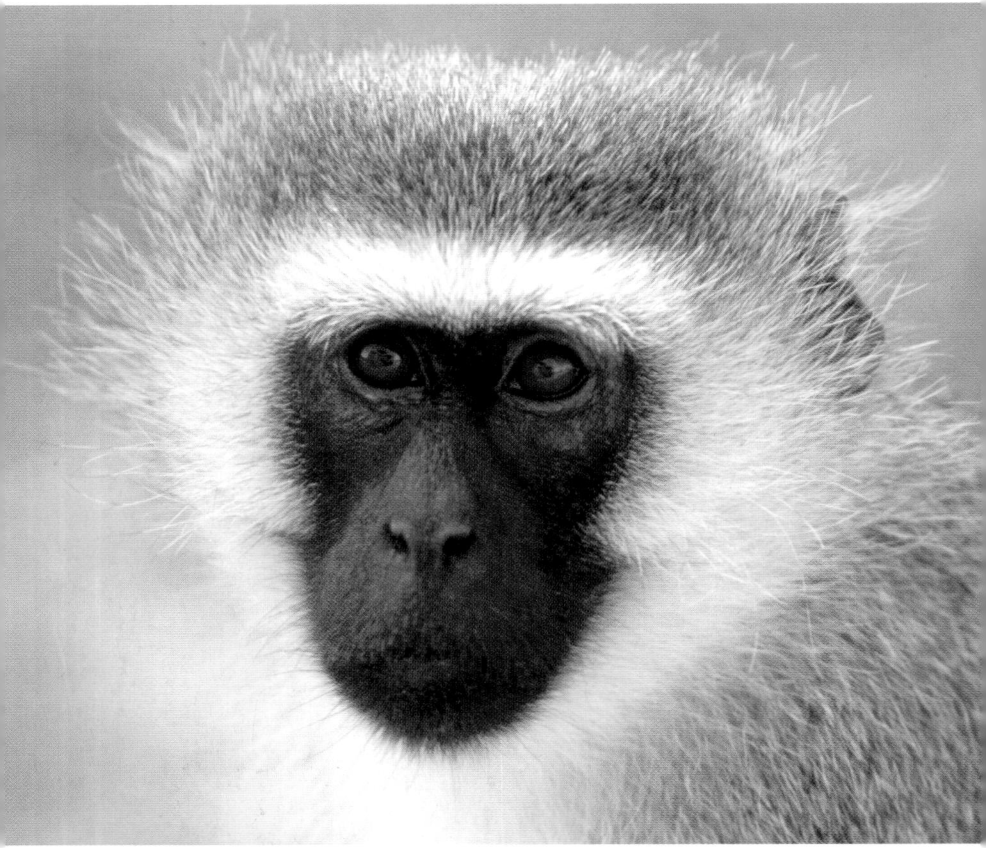